Uniform With This

———

STUDENTS' HANDBOOK
OF THE FACTS OF
ENGLISH LITERATURE

BY

J. F. A. PYRE, Ph.D.
THOMAS H. DICKINSON, Ph.D.
KARL YOUNG, Ph.D.

CENTURY READINGS

FOR A COURSE IN

ENGLISH LITERATURE